One W

A Most Concise Journal

Created and published by Knock Knock
Distributed by Who's There Inc.
Venice, CA 90291
knockknockstuff.com

ISBN: 978-160106365-6
UPC: 825703-50060-8

10 9 8 7 6 5 4

INTRODUCTION

Like most intelligent people, you've probably got a lot going on up there—and you may have occasionally considered keeping a journal to track it all. Perhaps you've even started journals, only to decide soon after that you're simply too busy living your life to write about it.

To be fair, rehashing the tedium of everyday life can be tiresome. Noted diarist Anaïs Nin observed, "We write to taste life twice." But what if your life these days tastes like rice cakes? Do you need to taste that twice?

Gentle Non-Journaler, we feel your anguish, and we have good news for you: keeping a journal does not necessarily mean recording every blink and exhalation. *It doesn't even have to mean writing.* Not really.

Let One Word a Day liberate you from the guilt of non-journaling—without obliging you to adopt a completely new lifestyle. With *this* low-maintenance journal, you simply choose a word to describe your day. One word.

If you're a real worrywart, you're already thinking: How am I supposed to pick one word to describe a whole day? That sounds harder than writing a whole sentence.

Fear not! You don't *have* to sum up your entire day. This One Word is *your* one word, and it can be whatever you like. Perhaps you'd like simply to reflect a singular aspect of your life for a year—your mood, creativity, or the state of your heart, for example. Or perhaps you'd like to choose a word to serve as shorthand for whatever preoccupies you most each day. "Mustard," "velvet," or "reactionary" could be smoke signals for whole worlds of experience, symbols you may enjoy decoding years later.

Most likely, your methods will evolve as the weeks pass. For those days when nothing comes to mind, consult the handy word list at the back of the book to help spark your imagination. However you determine each day, try to follow your gut, and select the word that feels most delicious to you in the moment—or at least deliciously honest. At year's end, not only will you have a uniquely personal objet d'art, but it will taste good, too.

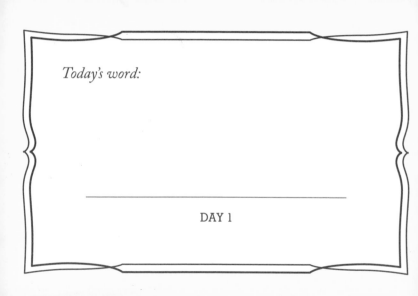

Today's word:

_____

DAY 1

Today's word:

_____

DAY 2

Today's word:

DAY 3

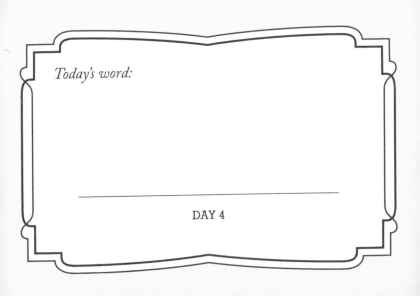

Today's word:

_____

DAY 4

Today's word:

_____

DAY 5

Today's word:

_____

DAY 6

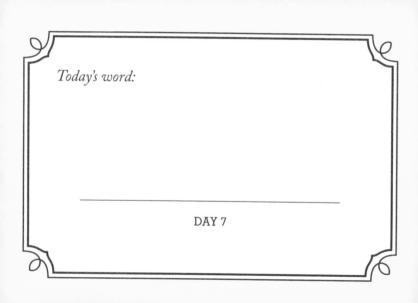

Today's word:

_____

DAY 7

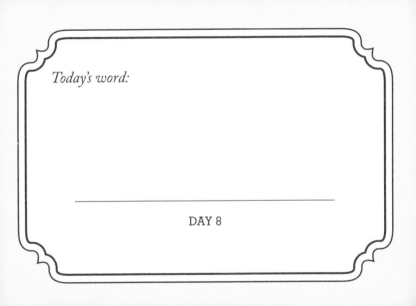

Today's word:

DAY 8

Today's word:

_____

DAY 9

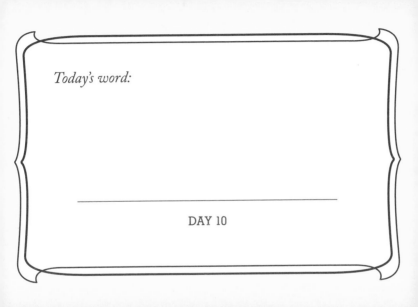

Today's word:

_____

DAY 10

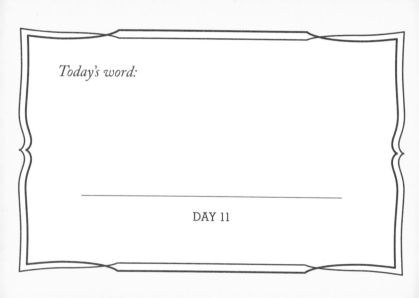

Today's word:

_____

DAY 11

Today's word:

_____

DAY 12

Today's word:

_____

DAY 13

Today's word:

_____

DAY 14

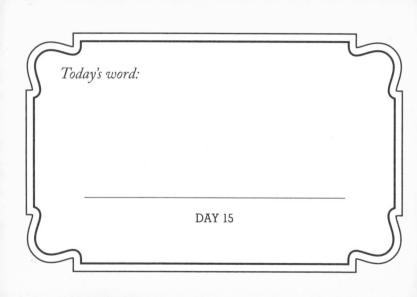

Today's word:

DAY 15

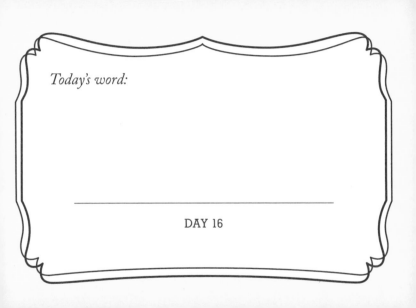

Today's word:

DAY 16

Today's word:

_____

DAY 17

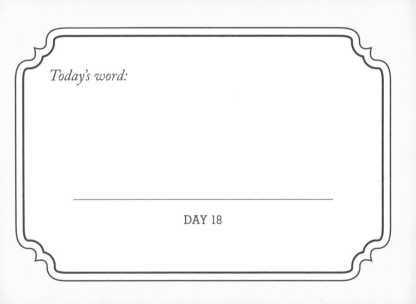

Today's word:

DAY 18

Today's word:

DAY 19

Today's word:

_____

DAY 20

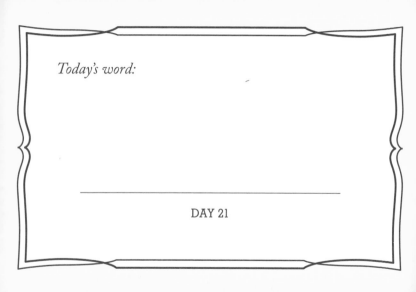

Today's word:

DAY 21

Today's word:

_____

DAY 22

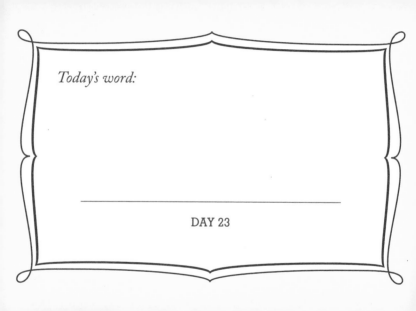

Today's word:

_____

DAY 23

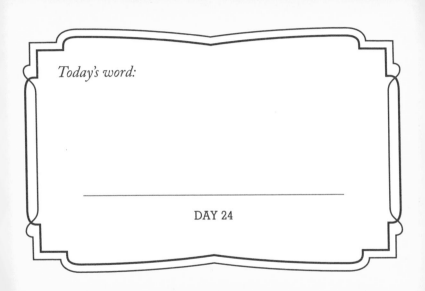

Today's word:

_____

DAY 24

Today's word:

_____

DAY 25

Today's word:

_____

DAY 26

Today's word:

_____

DAY 27

Today's word:

_____

DAY 28

Today's word:

_____

DAY 29

Today's word:

_____

DAY 30

Today's word:

_____

DAY 31

Today's word:

_____

DAY 32

Today's word:

_____

DAY 33

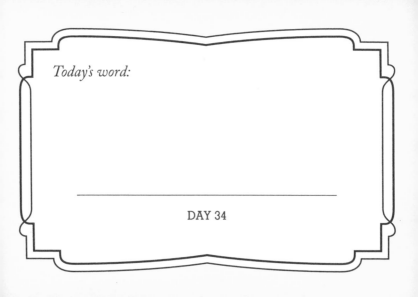

Today's word:

_____

DAY 34

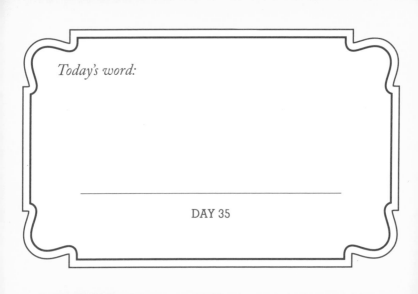

Today's word:

_____

DAY 35

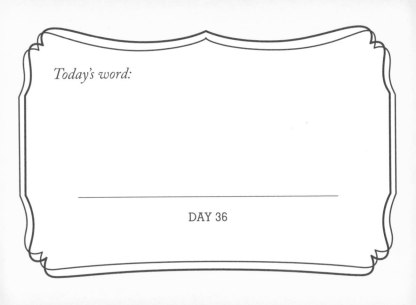

Today's word:

_____

DAY 36

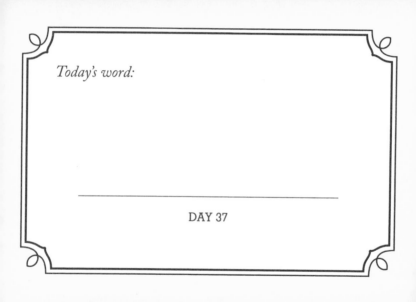

Today's word:

DAY 37

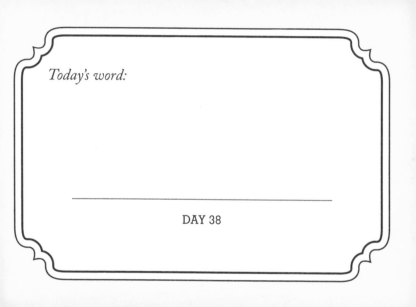

Today's word:

_____

DAY 38

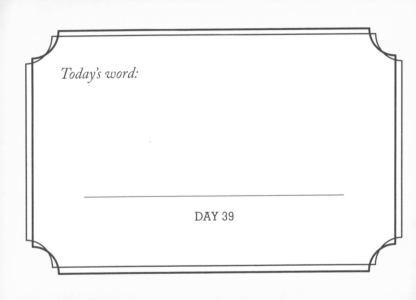

Today's word:

_____

DAY 39

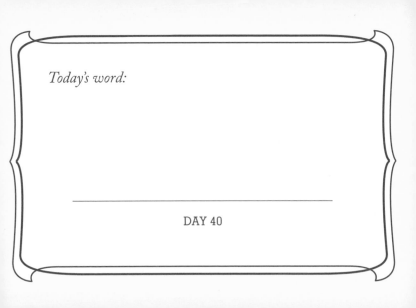

Today's word:

DAY 40

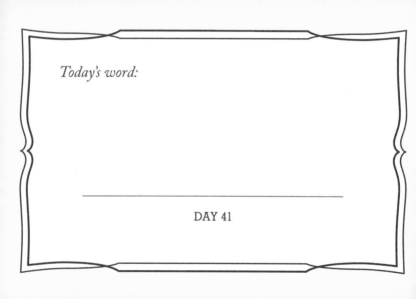

Today's word:

DAY 41

Today's word:

_____

DAY 42

Today's word:

_____

DAY 43

Today's word:

_____

DAY 44

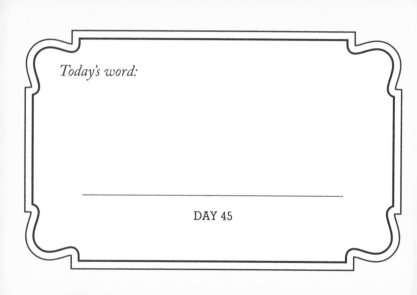

Today's word:

DAY 45

Today's word:

_____

DAY 46

Today's word:

_____

DAY 47

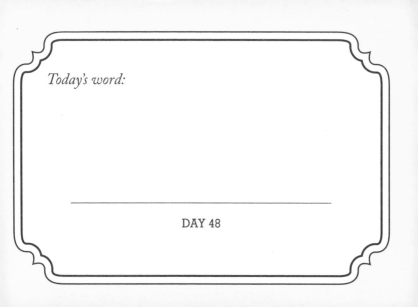

Today's word:

_____

DAY 48

Today's word:

_____

DAY 49

Today's word:

_____

DAY 50

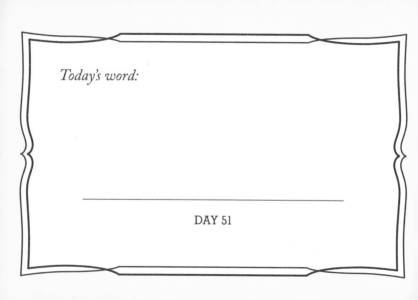

Today's word:

DAY 51

Today's word:

_____

DAY 52

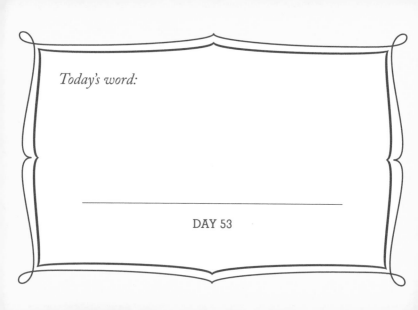

Today's word:

_____

DAY 53

Today's word:

_____

DAY 54

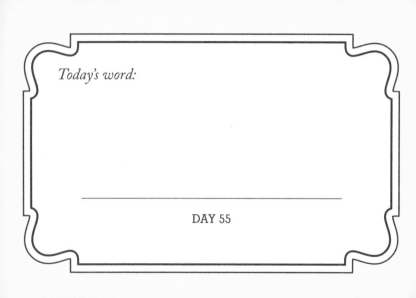

Today's word:

DAY 55

Today's word:

_____

DAY 56

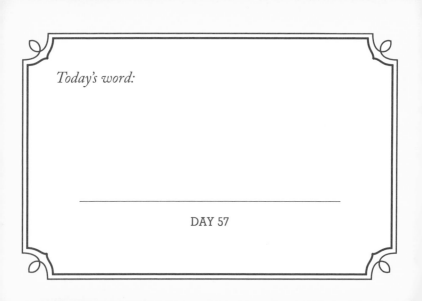

Today's word:

DAY 57

Today's word:

_____

DAY 58

Today's word:

_____

DAY 59

Today's word:

_____

DAY 60

Today's word:

_____

DAY 61

Today's word:

_____

DAY 62

Today's word:

_____

DAY 63

Today's word:

_____

DAY 64

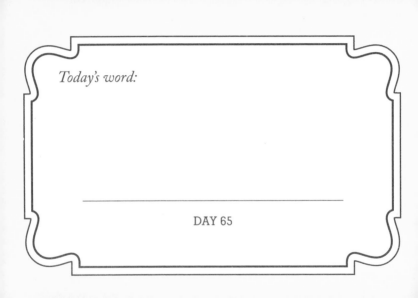

Today's word:

_____

DAY 65

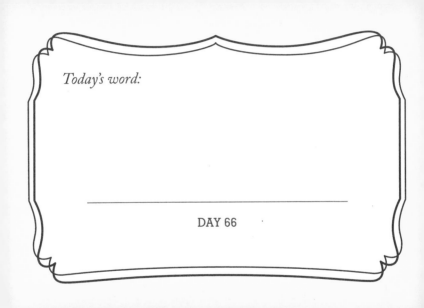

Today's word:

_____

DAY 66

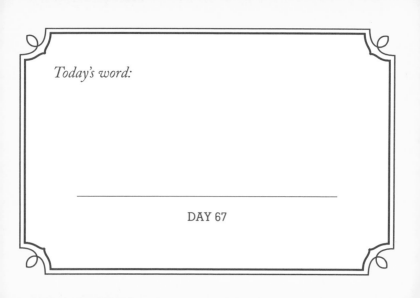

Today's word:

_____

DAY 67

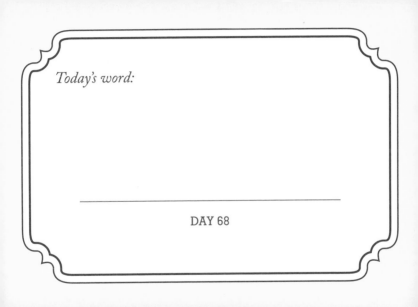

Today's word:

DAY 68

Today's word:

DAY 69

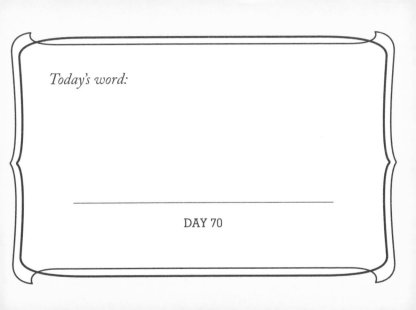

Today's word:

_____

DAY 70

Today's word:

_____

DAY 71

Today's word:

_____

DAY 72

Today's word:

_____

DAY 73

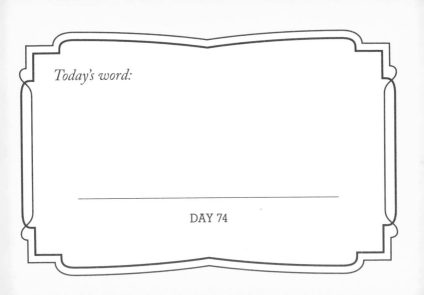

Today's word:

_____

DAY 74

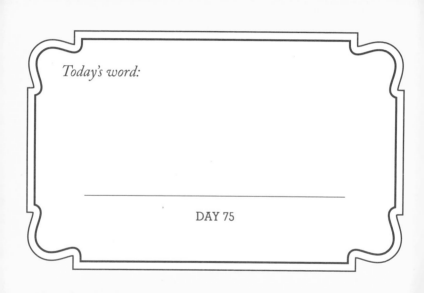

Today's word:

_____

DAY 75

Today's word:

_____

DAY 76

Today's word:

DAY 77

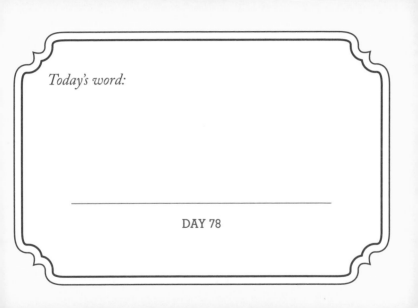

Today's word:

_____

DAY 78

Today's word:

_____

DAY 79

Today's word:

_____

DAY 80

Today's word:

_____

DAY 81

Today's word:

_____

DAY 82

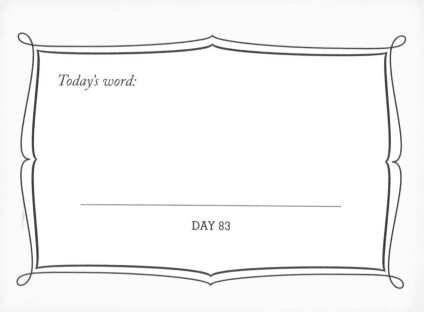

Today's word:

_____

DAY 83

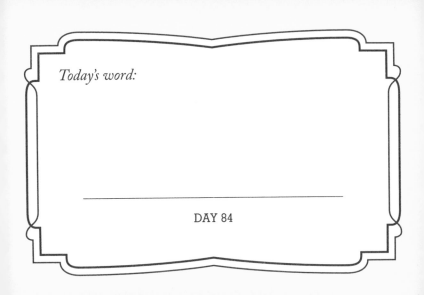

Today's word:

_____

DAY 84

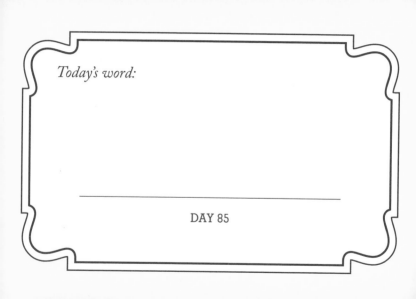

Today's word:

DAY 85

Today's word:

_____

DAY 86

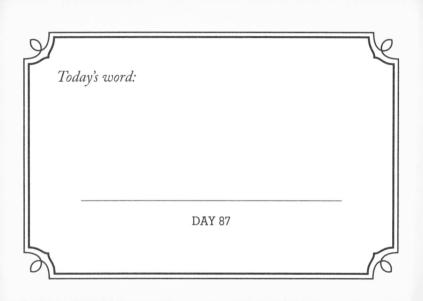

Today's word:

DAY 87

Today's word:

DAY 88

Today's word:

_____

DAY 89

Today's word:

_____

DAY 90

Today's word:

_____

DAY 91

Today's word:

_____

DAY 92

Today's word:

_____

DAY 93

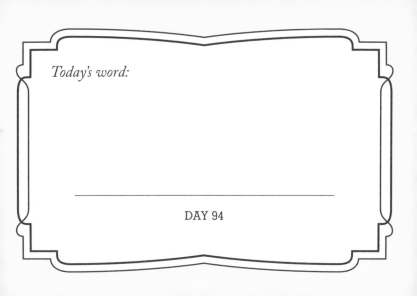

Today's word:

DAY 94

Today's word:

_____

DAY 95

Today's word:

_____

DAY 96

Today's word:

DAY 97

Today's word:

_____

DAY 98

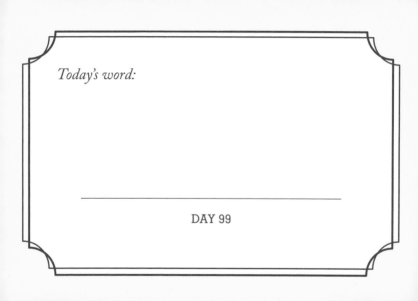

Today's word:

DAY 99

Today's word:

_____

DAY 100

Today's word:

_____

DAY 101

Today's word:

DAY 102

Today's word:

_____

DAY 103

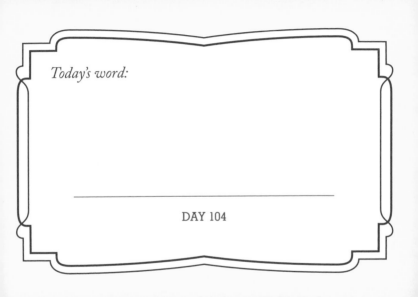

Today's word:

DAY 104

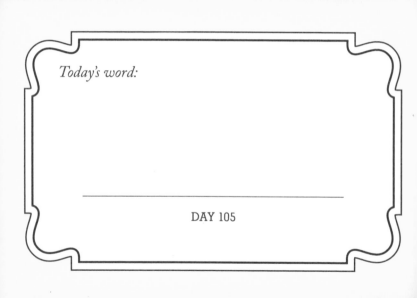

Today's word:

DAY 105

Today's word:

_____

DAY 106

Today's word:

_____

DAY 107

Today's word:

.

_____

DAY 108

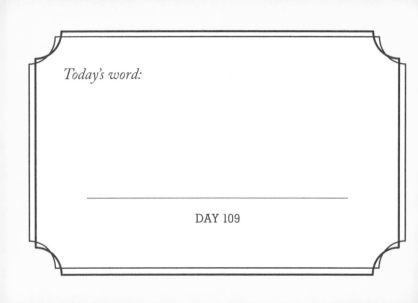

Today's word:

_____

DAY 109

Today's word:

DAY 110

Today's word:

_____

DAY 111

Today's word:

_____

DAY 112

Today's word:

_____

DAY 113

Today's word:

_____

DAY 114

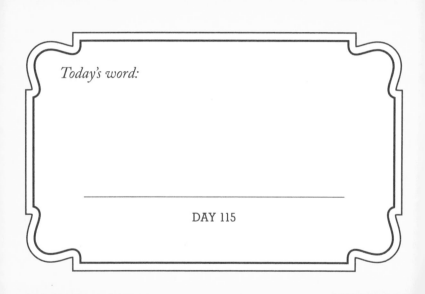

Today's word:

_____

DAY 115

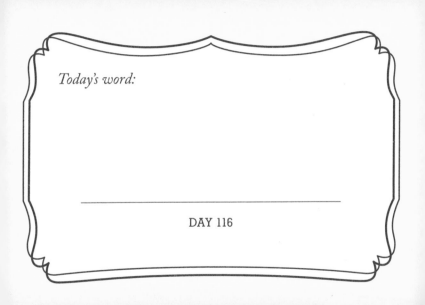

Today's word:

_____

DAY 116

Today's word:

_____

DAY 117

Today's word:

_____

DAY 118

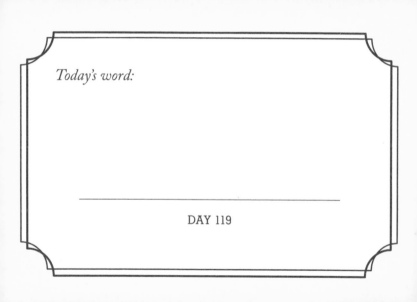

Today's word:

_____

DAY 119

Today's word:

_____

DAY 120

Today's word:

_____

DAY 121

Today's word:

_____

DAY 122

Today's word:

_____

DAY 123

Today's word:

_____

DAY 124

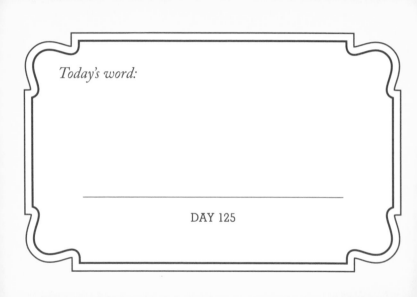

Today's word:

DAY 125

Today's word:

_____

DAY 126

Today's word:

_____

DAY 127

Today's word:

_____

DAY 128

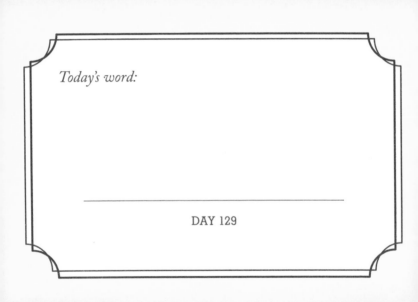

Today's word:

DAY 129

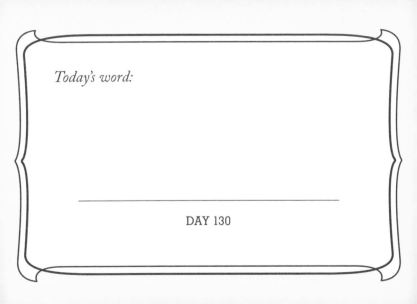

Today's word:

DAY 130

Today's word:

_____

DAY 131

Today's word:

_____

DAY 132

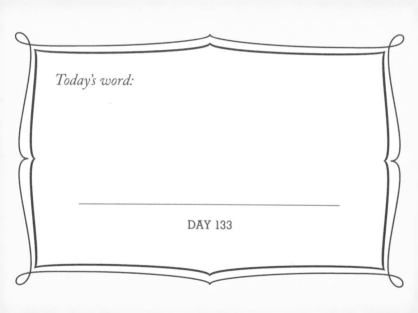

Today's word:

DAY 133

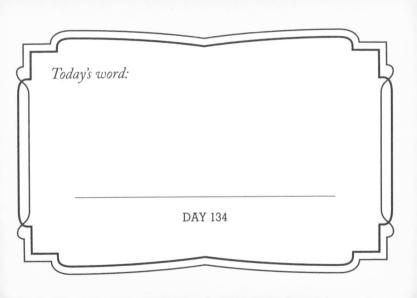

Today's word:

_____

DAY 134

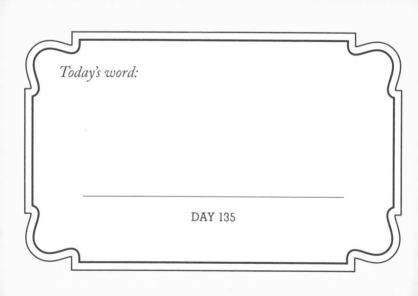

Today's word:

DAY 135

Today's word:

_____

DAY 136

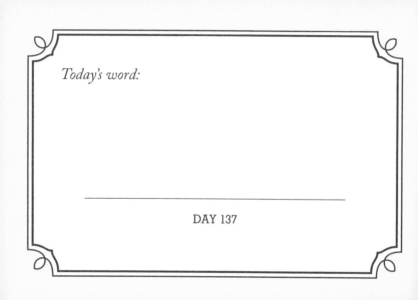

Today's word:

_____

DAY 137

Today's word:

_____

DAY 138

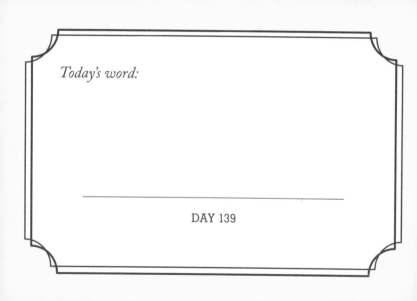

Today's word:

_____

DAY 139

Today's word:

_____

DAY 140

Today's word:

_____

DAY 141

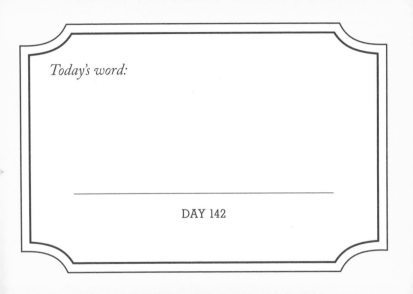

Today's word:

_____

DAY 142

Today's word:

_____

DAY 143

Today's word:

DAY 144

Today's word:

_____

DAY 145

Today's word:

_____

DAY 146

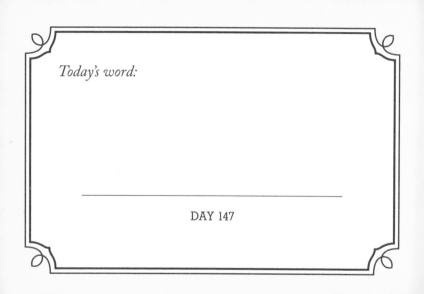

Today's word:

DAY 147

Today's word:

_____

DAY 148

Today's word:

_____

DAY 149

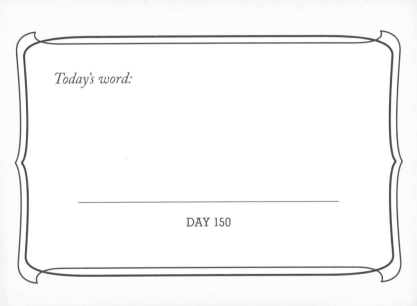

Today's word:

_____

DAY 150

Today's word:

_____

DAY 151

Today's word:

DAY 152

Today's word:

_____

DAY 153

Today's word:

_____

DAY 154

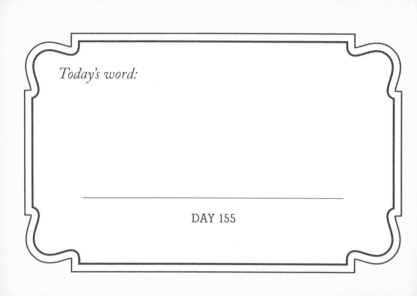

Today's word:

DAY 155

Today's word:

_____

DAY 156

Today's word:

_____

DAY 157

Today's word:

_____

DAY 158

Today's word:

_____

DAY 159

Today's word:

_____

DAY 160

Today's word:

_____

DAY 161

Today's word:

_____

DAY 162

Today's word:

_____

DAY 163

Today's word:

_____

DAY 164

Today's word:

_____

DAY 165

Today's word:

_____

DAY 166

Today's word:

_____

DAY 167

Today's word:

_____

DAY 168

Today's word:

_____

DAY 169

Today's word:

_____

DAY 170

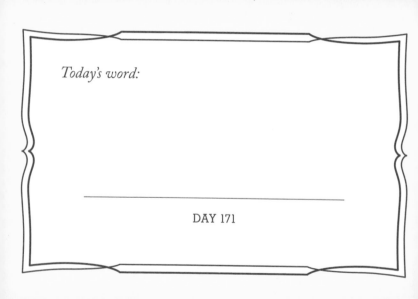

Today's word:

_____

DAY 171

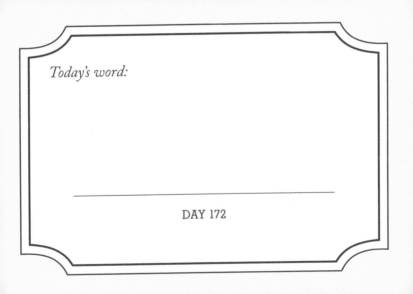

Today's word:

_____

DAY 172

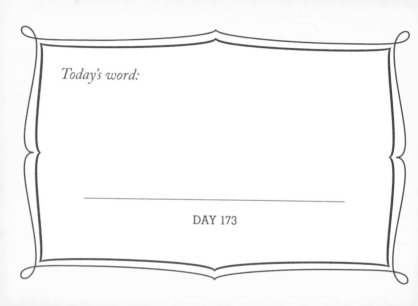

Today's word:

_____

DAY 173

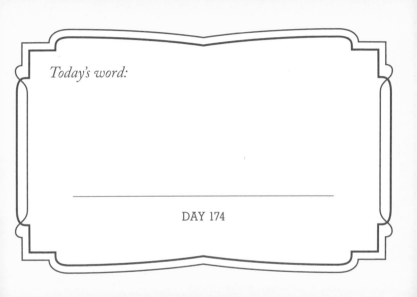

Today's word:

DAY 174

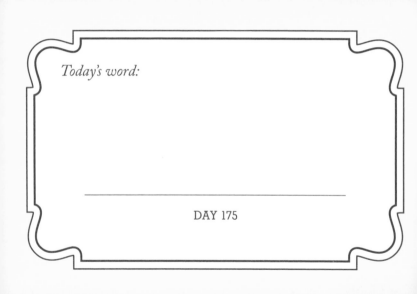

Today's word:

_____

DAY 175

Today's word:

_____

DAY 176

Today's word:

<hr />

DAY 177

Today's word:

_____

DAY 178

Today's word:

_____

DAY 179

Today's word:

_____

DAY 180

Today's word:

_____

DAY 181

Today's word:

_____

DAY 182

Today's word:

_____

DAY 183

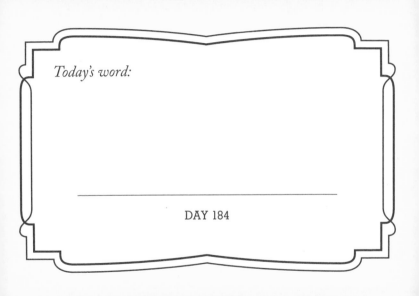

Today's word:

_____

DAY 184

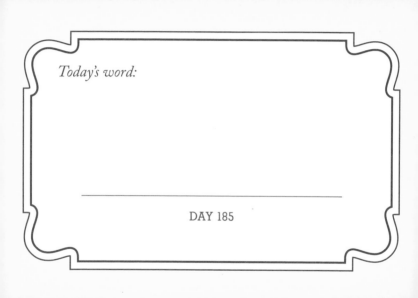

Today's word:

_____

DAY 185

Today's word:

_____

DAY 186

Today's word:

_____

DAY 187

Today's word:

_____

DAY 188

Today's word:

_____

DAY 189

Today's word:

_____

DAY 190

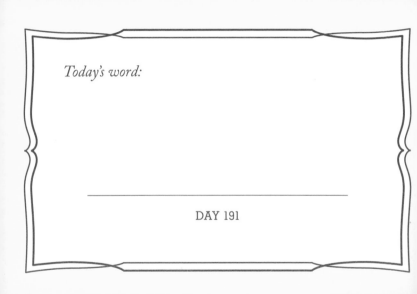

Today's word:

_____

DAY 191

Today's word:

_____

DAY 192

Today's word:

_____

DAY 193

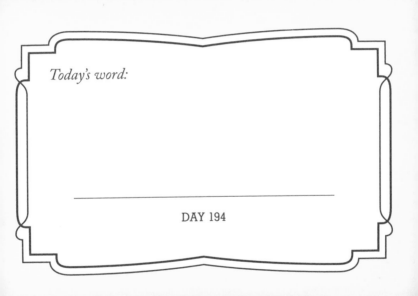

Today's word:

DAY 194

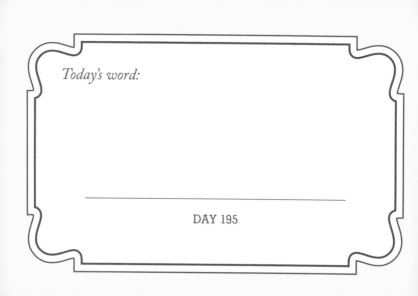

Today's word:

_____

DAY 195

Today's word:

_____

DAY 196

Today's word:

_____

DAY 197

Today's word:

_____

DAY 198

Today's word:

_____

DAY 199

Today's word:

_____

DAY 200

Today's word:

_____

DAY 201

Today's word:

_____

DAY 202

Today's word:

_____

DAY 203

Today's word:

_____

DAY 204

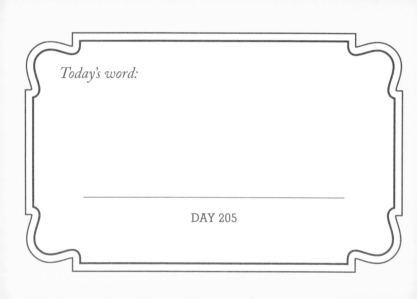

Today's word:

DAY 205

Today's word:

_____

DAY 206

Today's word:

_____

DAY 207

Today's word:

_____

DAY 208

Today's word:

_____

DAY 209

Today's word:

_____

DAY 210

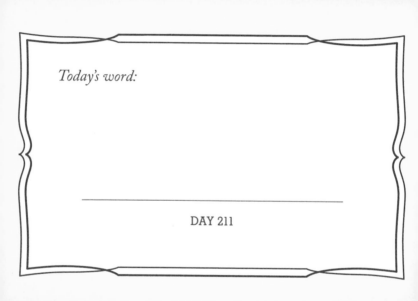

Today's word:

_____

DAY 211

Today's word:

_____

DAY 212

Today's word:

_____

DAY 213

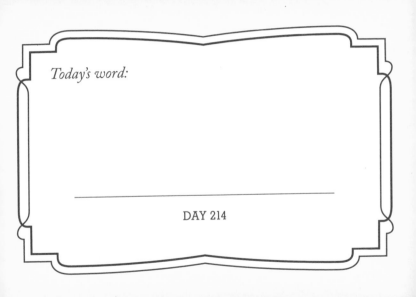

Today's word:

DAY 214

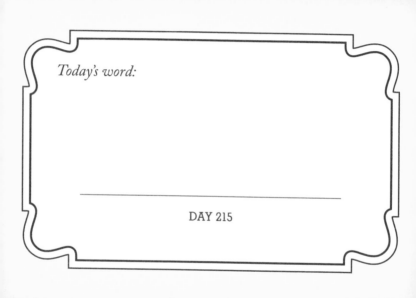

Today's word:

DAY 215

Today's word:

_____

DAY 216

Today's word:

_____

DAY 217

Today's word:

_____

DAY 218

Today's word:

_____

DAY 219

Today's word:

_____

DAY 220

Today's word:

_____

DAY 221

Today's word:

_____

DAY 222

Today's word:

_____

DAY 223

Today's word:

_____

DAY 224

Today's word:

_____

DAY 225

Today's word:

_____

DAY 226

Today's word:

_____

DAY 227

Today's word:

_____

DAY 228

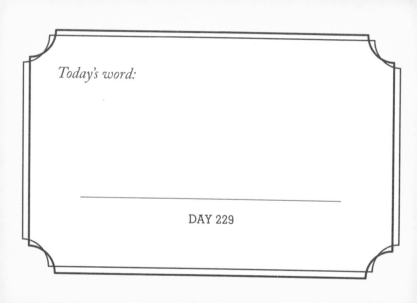

Today's word:

DAY 229

Today's word:

_____

DAY 230

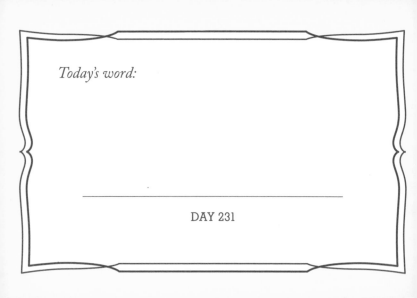

Today's word:

_____

DAY 231

Today's word:

_____

DAY 232

Today's word:

_____

DAY 233

Today's word:

_____

DAY 234

Today's word:

_____

DAY 235

Today's word:

_____

DAY 236

Today's word:

_____

DAY 237

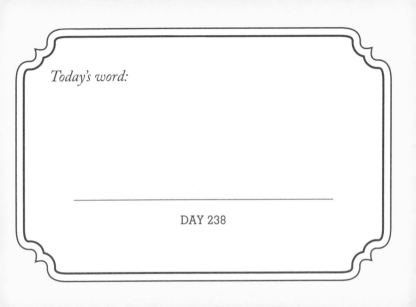

Today's word:

_____

DAY 238

Today's word:

_____

DAY 239

Today's word:

_____

DAY 240

Today's word:

_____

DAY 241

Today's word:

_____

DAY 242

Today's word:

_____

DAY 243

Today's word:

_____

DAY 244

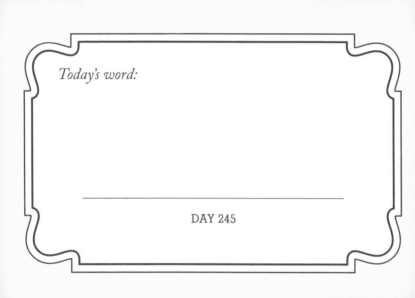

Today's word:

_____

DAY 245

Today's word:

_____

DAY 246

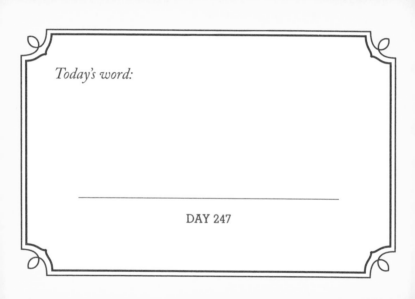

Today's word:

_____

DAY 247

Today's word:

DAY 248

Today's word:

_____

DAY 249

Today's word:

_____

DAY 250

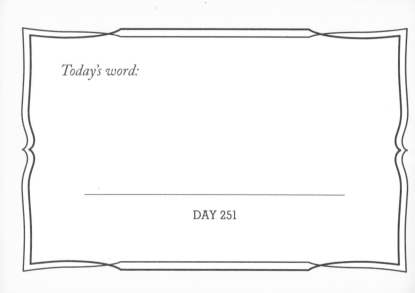

Today's word:

_____

DAY 251

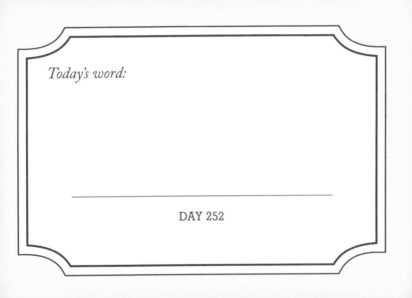

Today's word:

_____

DAY 252

Today's word:

_____

DAY 253

Today's word:

_____

DAY 254

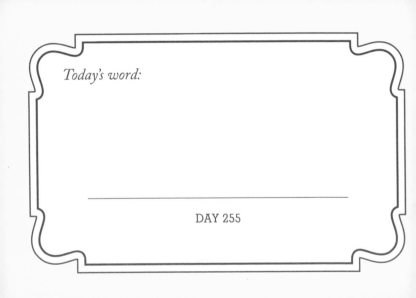

Today's word:

DAY 255

Today's word:

_____

DAY 256

Today's word:

_____

DAY 257

Today's word:

_____

DAY 258

Today's word:

_____

DAY 259

Today's word:

_____

DAY 260

Today's word:

_____

DAY 261

Today's word:

_____

DAY 262

Today's word:

_____

DAY 263

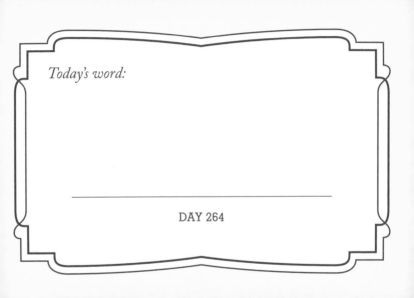

Today's word:

DAY 264

Today's word:

_____

DAY 265

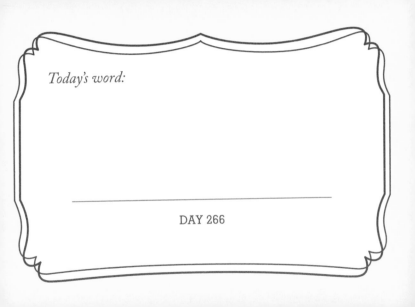

Today's word:

DAY 266

Today's word:

_____

DAY 267

Today's word:

_____

DAY 268

Today's word:

DAY 269

Today's word:

_____

DAY 270

Today's word:

_____

DAY 271

Today's word:

_____

DAY 272

Today's word:

_____

DAY 273

Today's word:

DAY 274

Today's word:

_____

DAY 275

Today's word:

_____

DAY 276

Today's word:

_____

DAY 277

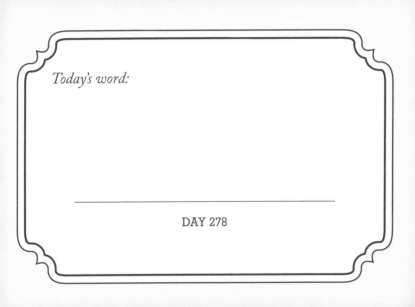

Today's word:

_____

DAY 278

Today's word:

_____

DAY 279

Today's word:

_____

DAY 280

Today's word:

_____

DAY 281

Today's word:

_____

DAY 282

Today's word:

_____

DAY 283

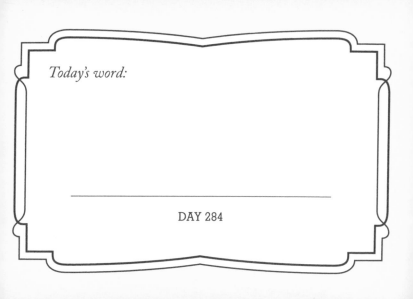

Today's word:

_____

DAY 284

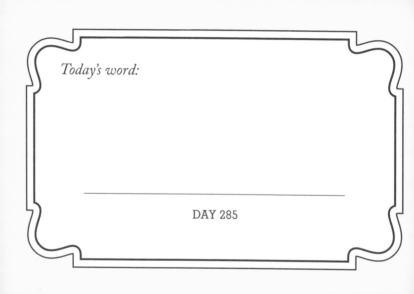

Today's word:

_____

DAY 285

Today's word:

_____

DAY 286

Today's word:

_____

DAY 287

Today's word:

_____

DAY 288

Today's word:

_____

DAY 289

Today's word:

_____

DAY 290

Today's word:

_____

DAY 291

Today's word:

DAY 292

Today's word:

_____

DAY 293

Today's word:

DAY 294

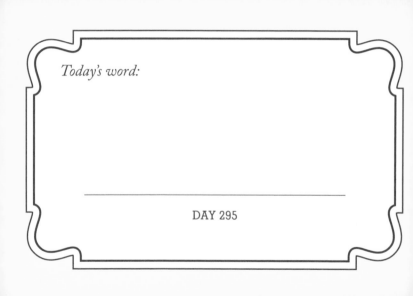

Today's word:

_____

DAY 295

Today's word:

_____

DAY 296

Today's word:

_____

DAY 297

Today's word:

_____

DAY 298

Today's word:

_____

DAY 299

Today's word:

_____

DAY 300

Today's word:

_____

DAY 301

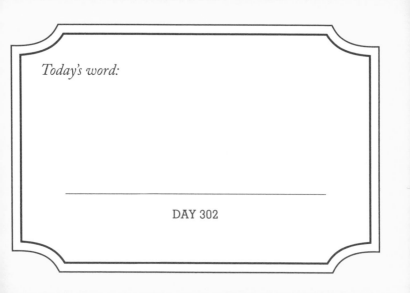

Today's word:

DAY 302

Today's word:

_____

DAY 303

Today's word:

DAY 304

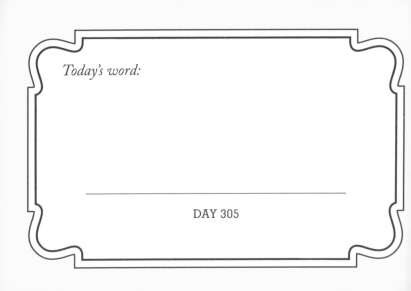

Today's word:

DAY 305

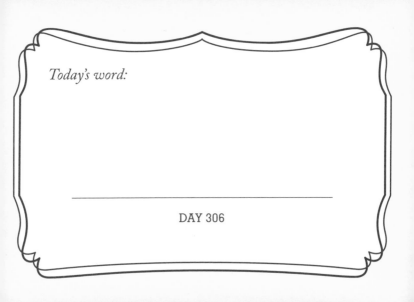

Today's word:

_____

DAY 306

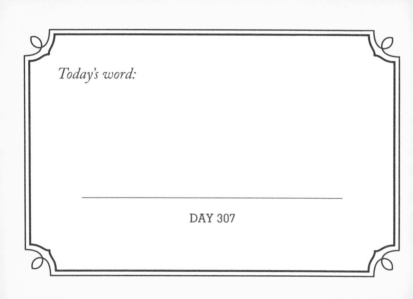

Today's word:

_____

DAY 307

Today's word:

_____

DAY 308

Today's word:

DAY 309

Today's word:

_____

DAY 310

Today's word:

_____

DAY 311

Today's word:

_____

DAY 312

Today's word:

_____

DAY 313

Today's word:

_____

DAY 314

Today's word:

_____

DAY 315

Today's word:

_____

DAY 316

Today's word:

_____

DAY 317

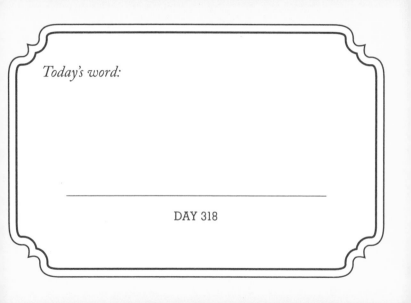

Today's word:

_____

DAY 318

Today's word:

_____

DAY 319

Today's word:

_____

DAY 320

Today's word:

<hr>

DAY 321

Today's word:

_____

DAY 322

Today's word:

_____

DAY 323

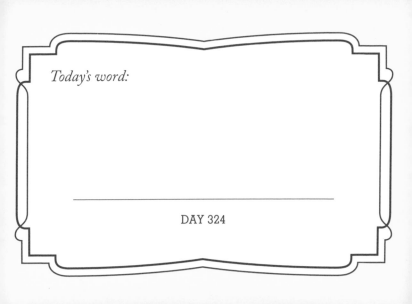

Today's word:

_____

DAY 324

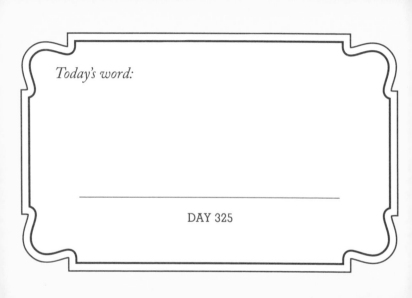

Today's word:

_____

DAY 325

Today's word:

_____

DAY 326

Today's word:

_____

DAY 327

Today's word:

_____

DAY 328

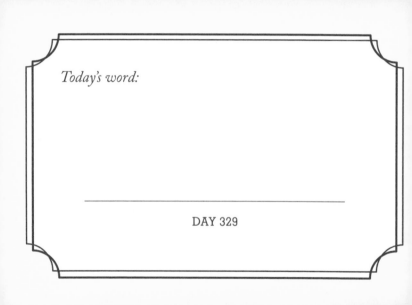

Today's word:

_____

DAY 329

Today's word:

_____

DAY 330

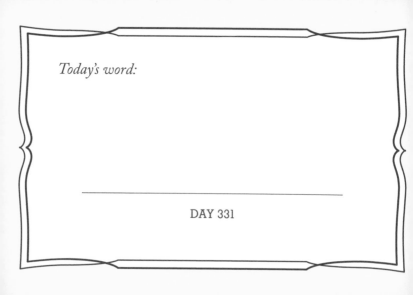

Today's word:

_____

DAY 331

Today's word:

_____

DAY 332

Today's word:

_____

DAY 333

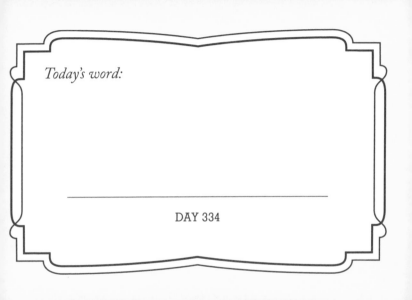

Today's word:

_____

DAY 334

Today's word:

_____

DAY 335

Today's word:

_____

DAY 336

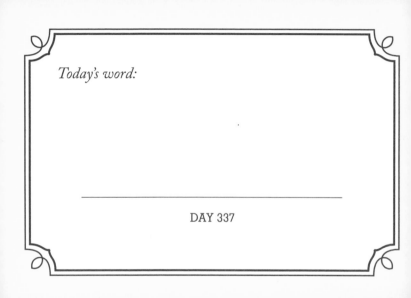

Today's word:

DAY 337

Today's word:

_____

DAY 338

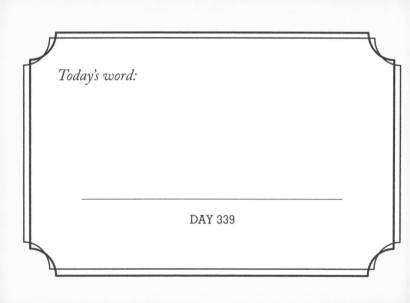

Today's word:

_____

DAY 339

Today's word:

_____

DAY 340

Today's word:

_____

DAY 341

Today's word:

_____

DAY 342

Today's word:

_____

DAY 343

Today's word:

_____

DAY 344

Today's word:

_____

DAY 345

Today's word:

_____

DAY 346

Today's word:

_____

DAY 347

Today's word:

_____

DAY 348

Today's word:

_____

DAY 349

Today's word:

_____

DAY 350

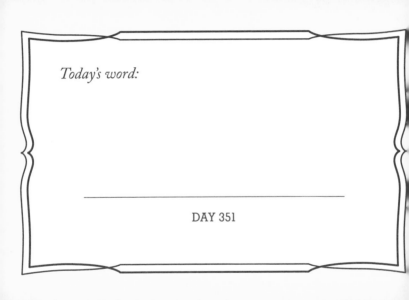

Today's word:

DAY 351

Today's word:

_____

DAY 352

Today's word:

_____

DAY 353

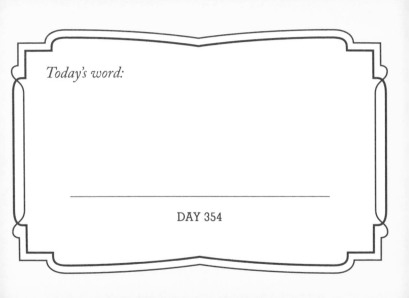

Today's word:

DAY 354

Today's word:

DAY 355

Today's word:

_____

DAY 356

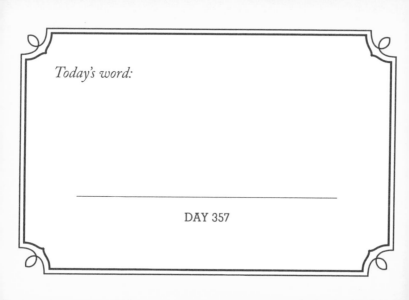

Today's word:

_____

DAY 357

Today's word:

_____

DAY 358

Today's word:

_____

DAY 359

Today's word:

_____

DAY 360

Today's word:

_____

DAY 361

Today's word:

_____

DAY 362

Today's word:

_____

DAY 363

Today's word:

_____

DAY 364

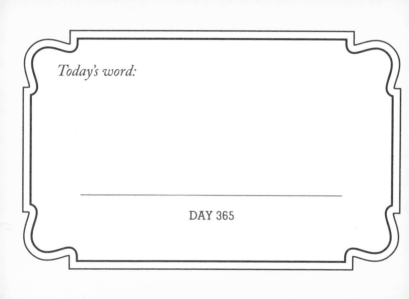

Today's word:

_____

DAY 365

HANDY WORD LIST

If you're at a loss for you-know-what, peruse this list! These
words may be used to describe your day, your state of
mind, or your activities. Some entries are just random,
because some days are just like that.

THE CLASSICS

ANNOYED	AWESOME	BLUE	BORING
Bitchy	Beautiful	Delicate	Blah
Cantankerous	Crackerjack	Depressed	Bland
Crotchety	Excellent	Ennui	Humdrum
Grumpy	Fantastic	Funk	Mind-numbing
Irked	Glorious	Glum	Monotonous
Misanthropic	Marvelous	Hormonal	Pedestrian
Peevish	Remarkable	Malaise	Prosaic
Stabby	Sensational	Melancholy	Routine
Sullen	Smashing	Wistful	Snoozeville
Testy	Wonderful	Woebegone	Tedious

THE CLASSICS

BUSY	CALM	CELEBRATION	CONFIDENT
Absorbed	Balmy	Blowout	Bullish
Bustling	Halcyon	Ceremony	Dauntless
Buzzing	Mellow	Commemoration	Emboldened
Diligent	Mild	Debauch	Fortified
Engaged	Placid	Fiesta	Gutsy
Engrossed	Restful	Hoedown	Heroic
Hopping	Serene	Saturnalia	Intrepid
Humming	Soothing	Shindig	Nervy
Immersed	Tranquil	Soiree	Resolute
Lively	Zen	Wing-ding	Valiant

THE CLASSICS

CONFUSED	ENERGETIC	EXCITING	EXHAUSTED
Baffled	Dynamic	Bracing	Bushed
Befuddled	Frisky	Electrifying	Drained
Bemused	Gingery	Exhilarating	Enervated
Bewildered	Jaunty	Galvanizing	Pooped
Boggled	Peppy	Invigorating	Run-down
Confounded	Robust	Rejuvenating	Sluggish
Discombobulated	Spirited	Rip-snorting	Spent
Muddled	Sprightly	Rousing	Tuckered
Mystified	Vivacious	Stimulating	Weary
Perplexed	Zippy	Thrilling	Worn-out

THE CLASSICS

FRUSTRATED	FUN	FUNNY	GOOD
Confounded	Blithe	Amusing	Copacetic
Defeated	Bouyant	Antic	Dandy
Discouraged	Chummy	Comic	Ducky
Disheartened	Expansive	Droll	Gratifying
Exasperated	Frolicsome	Farcical	Groovy
Foiled	Genial	Humorous	Heartening
Hindered	Gregarious	Hysterical	Hunky-dory
Shackled	Jubilant	Riotous	Peachy
Stultified	Mirthful	Sidesplitting	Pleasing
Thwarted	Tickled	Witty	Satisfying

THE CLASSICS

HARD	LAZY	LOVING	PERTURBED
Arduous	Lackadaisical	Adoring	Appalled
Backbreaking	Laggard	Affectionate	Cheesed
Brutal	Languid	Devoted	Cross
Demanding	Languorous	Doting	Fuming
Excruciating	Lethargic	Empathetic	Indignant
Grueling	Listless	Fond	Miffed
Herculean	Lumpish	Motherly	Piqued
Killer	Shiftless	Nurturing	Rankled
Murderous	Slothful	Tender	Steamed
Tough	Torpid	Warm	Ticked

THE CLASSICS

POSITIVE	PRODUCTIVE	ROMANTIC	SICK
Heartened	Constructive	Amorous	Afflicted
Idealistic	Fertile	Ardent	Debilitated
Inspired	Fruitful	Besotted	Faint
Optimistic	Groundbreaking	Bewitched	Feeble
Plucky	Imaginative	Enchanted	Ill
Rose-colored	Industrious	Erotic	Infirm
Sanguine	Inventive	Fevered	Insubstantial
Spunky	Kick-ass	Pining	Punk
Sunny	Prolific	Sizzling	Queasy
Upbeat	Visionary	Starry-eyed	Toxic

THE CLASSICS

SPACY	STRESSED	SUCKY	SURPRISED
Airy	Agitated	Abysmal	Amazed
Dazed	Burnt	Atrocious	Astonished
Distracted	Crispy	Cruddy	Astounded
Dreamy	Frazzled	Dreadful	Blindsided
Flaky	Harried	Ghastly	Dumbfounded
Foggy	Inundated	Gruesome	Flabbergasted
Moonstruck	Overbooked	Loathsome	Floored
Punchy	Overwhelmed	Rotten	Startled
Scatterbrained	Pinched	Sour	Stupefied
Zoned-out	Swamped	Subpar	Thunderstruck

THE CLASSICS

WEATHER	WEIRD	WORK	WORRIED
Arctic	Bizarre	Craft	Antsy
Blazing	Curious	Discipline	Anxious
Blustery	Freakish	Drudgery	Concerned
Bracing	Funky	Elbow grease	Distressed
Misty	Oddish	Grind	Flustered
Muggy	Off-kilter	Labor	Fretful
Stormy	Peculiar	Métier	Preoccupied
Sultry	Queer	Moil	Troubled
Sweltering	Screwy	Sweat	Uneasy
Torrential	Surreal	Toil	Unnerved

GRAB BAG

ABUNDANT	BLOCKHEAD	COZY	DRIVE
Bountiful	Clod	Comfy	Bus
Copious	Cretin	Domestic	Chauffeur
Fecund	Dingbat	Homebody	Commute
Fruitful	Dolt	Homey	Joyride
Fulsome	Dumbbell	Nesting	Motor
Lavish	Looby	Safe	Shepherd
Overflowing	Meathead	Sheltered	Taxi
Rich	Nudnick	Snug	Tool
Sumptuous	Oaf	Toasty	Wheel
Wealthy	Woodenhead	Warmed	Whirl

GRAB BAG

FIGHT	FLIRTY	GOSSIP	HEALING
Brawl	Coquettish	Clishmaclaver	Curative
Collieshangie	Coy	Hateration	Elixir
Donnybrook	Cute	Jaw	Liniment
Dustup	Frisky	Kibitz	Ointment
Fisticuffs	Kittenish	Quidnunc	Panacea
Fracas	Minxish	Schmooze	Potion
Imbroglio	Seductive	Scuttlebutt	Remedy
Rumble	Siren	Smack	Restorative
Skirmish	Teasing	Tommyrot	Salve
Tussle	Vampish	Yenta	Therapy

GRAB BAG

HUNGRY	INSTINCTIVE	INTOXICATED	LUCKY
Craving	Animal	Boozed	Auspicious
Famished	Clairvoyant	Buzzed	Blessed
Gluttonous	Empathic	Crapulent	Charmed
Gormandizing	Gut	Hammered	Fluky
Insatiable	Intuitive	Loaded	Fortuitous
Peckish	Natural	Mellow	Fortunate
Piggy	Presentient	Smashed	Golden
Ravenous	Psychic	Soused	Heaven-sent
Starved	Spontaneous	Tipsy	Providential
Voracious	Visceral	Wasted	Serendipitous

GRAB BAG

MEAL	MESS	MISCHIEF	MYSTERIOUS
Banquet	Botch	Capers	Ambiguous
Binge	Clutter	Chicanery	Cloaked
Chow	Foul-up	Hijinks	Eerie
Clambake	Havoc	Hocus-pocus	Enigmatic
Feast	Mishmash	Monkeyshines	Esoteric
Glut	Morass	Rabble-rousing	Inscrutable
Nosh	Muddle	Razzle-dazzle	Misty
Relish	Rumple	Shenanigans	Murky
Repast	Shambles	Skylarking	Nebulous
Smorgasbord	Snafu	Tomfoolery	Obscure

GRAB BAG

NEUROTIC	PAMPERING	PERFECTION	POISED
Aggro	Baby	Classic	Balanced
Hysterical	Comfort	Flawless	Collected
Manic	Decompress	Ideal	Composed
Masochistic	Indulge	Paragon	Cool
Narcissistic	Luxuriate	Pink	Even-keeled
OCD	Pleasure	Pinnacle	Forbearing
Paranoid	Revel	Summit	Grounded
Schizo	Soothe	Superlative	Self-possessed
Touched	Spoil	Supreme	Stoic
Unhinged	Treat	Ultimate	Unflappable

GRAB BAG

PROFANITY	SANCTUARY	SCARED	SHY
Bawdry	Asylum	Alarmed	Antisocial
Curse	Harbor	Cowering	Bashful
Cuss	Haven	Fazed	Introverted
Epithet	Hideaway	Horrified	Meek
Expletive	Hideout	Intimidated	Reclusive
Indecency	Refuge	Panicked	Reserved
Obscenity	Retreat	Shocked	Reticent
Pottymouth	Sanctum	Startled	Self-conscious
Saltiness	Shelter	Stunned	Sheepish
Vulgarity	Shrine	Terrified	Withdrawn

GRAB BAG

SPIRITUAL	THOUGHTFUL	TRAVEL	UNCERTAIN
Celestial	Clearheaded	Jet-setter	Conflicted
Cosmic	Contemplative	Junket	Dubious
Ineffable	Discerning	Migrate	Equivocating
Karmic	Meditative	Nomadic	Hesitant
Metaphysical	Pensive	Roam	Oscillating
Mystical	Philosophical	Sojourn	Shilly-shallying
Numinous	Sagacious	Trek	Tentative
Reverent	Sage	Vagabond	Vacillating
Sacred	Shrewd	Wanderlust	Wary
Transcendent	Sober	Wayfare	Wavering

GRAB BAG

WACKY	WATER	WHIMSICAL	YUMMY
Bedlam	Cascade	Capricious	Ambrosial
Bonkers	Current	Fanciful	Creamy
Cockeyed	Pond	Fickle	Delectable
Cuckoo	Puddle	Flighty	Juicy
Daffy	Rivulet	Impulsive	Luscious
Daft	Sluice	Mercurial	Nectarean
Loony	Swell	Mischievous	Spicy
Madcap	Tide	Playful	Succulent
Screwball	Waterfall	Quirky	Tangy
Zany	Wave	Quixotic	Toothsome